P9-BYW-366

Weekly Reader Children's Book Club presents

RUNAWAY PONY, RUNAWAY DOG

by Ruth and Latrobe Carroll
pictures by Ruth Carroll

New York   HENRY Z. WALCK, INC.

Copyright © 1963 by Ruth and Latrobe Carroll
All rights reserved
Library of Congress Catalog Card Number: 63-17188
WEEKLY READER BOOK CLUB EDITION
INTERMEDIATE DIVISION

1

TOUGH ENOUGH whined. The little dog was worried. He cocked his large ears forward; his eyes were restless, alert. He knew something was wrong with Sassy, his pony friend. The pony was limping toward a tempting clump of grass. Tough Enough was trotting along beside him. When the pony put his nose down to the grass, the dog whimpered softly and touched Sassy's nose with his.

All of a sudden, Tough Enough's ears brought him news. He turned them toward distant sounds. As he listened he stopped and stood quite still with his left paw lifted a little. People were coming into this pasture high in the Great Smoky Mountains. They were still a long way off, but he began to bark, sharp and loud and challenging. He sniffed and sniffed, trying to catch their scent. Who were these people? Why had they come? He licked the end of his asking nose so he could smell things better.

Now, along the coolness of the morning breeze, he caught familiar scents. His barking changed from a shrill warning to an excited sound of welcome. *His* people were coming—his master, Beanie Tatum, and Beanie's mother and father and Beanie's brothers, Buck and Irby, and Beanie's sisters, Serena and Annie Mae.

Tough Enough ran toward them, faster and faster. He bounded over a jutting rock, over a fallen tree. He hurled himself up on Beanie as high as he could leap, pawing him and doing his best to lick a great deal of him. Then he went tearing round and round him in joyful yelping circles.

He stopped so quickly, he skidded. His nose had brought him a new scent. A stranger, a man he hadn't noticed in his eager rush, was with the Tatums. Now the little dog saw him; he gave an inquisitive yip and began to walk toward him slowly. He sensed that his people had accepted this stranger, but he wanted to try a nose test. He sidled up behind, close to the man's ankles, and sniffed at the edge of his overalls. His nose had trouble sorting out all the scents it was sucking in—smells of cows, of a goat, of sheep and of pigs.

Pa Tatum was talking to the stranger. "Jed, we can't figure what's ailin' Beanie's pony, but you're the doctor. He hasn't got a sharp stone or anything stuck up in his hoof, far as I can see—no, sir, he's not graveled the way he was when he was a little wild pony on the Outer Banks and we picked him up. No bones broke. But just look at him a-limpin' over yonder—a-limpin' in his right foreleg like he's bad hurt."

6

"Well, let's look him over," said Jed. He was an animal doctor, a veterinarian.

Sassy was hobbling toward Beanie. When he got close he nuzzled Beanie's neck, then he began to push his nose against Beanie's pockets, hunting for an apple or a carrot.

Beanie took hold of Sassy's halter and led him toward the animal doctor. He coaxed him to stand still, petting him and talking to him so the pony wouldn't mind strange hands touching him and even hurting him, perhaps.

Jed lifted the pony's right foreleg. He looked at it and at the shoulder above, pressing lightly here and there; then he examined the hoof.

Tough Enough was watching his every move, tilting his head and whining now and then.

"He most likely strained a tendon," said Jed. "Tell you what. Fetch him down to my hospital and put him in the pasture close to the stable. I'll keep an eye on him. That way I'll find out what's ailin' him."

"Sure thing, Doc," said Pa. "We'd best bring the little dog, Tough Enough, too. The two of 'em just plumb go together, stick to each other like a fly sticks to flypaper."

Jed nodded. "Well, good. That way the horse will be quiet, like."

Pa said, "Hope you won't have a time with them

two. Beanie's made such a fuss over 'em, pettin' 'em and all, you'll maybe find 'em a handful."

After the animal doctor had gone, Pa backed the old Tatum truck out from under a shed. He and Beanie's oldest brother, Buck, set a stout wooden ramp in place, then Beanie led Sassy up into the truck with the dog following close behind.

When the two animals were safely in, Pa and Buck pulled the ramp up inside. They fitted it into slots so it made a box stall for Sassy. With a piece of rope, Beanie tied the pony's halter to a wooden slat. He patted the pony's nose with gentle fingers. "Now don't you fret yourself," he said. "We're fixin' to get you well."

Tough Enough stayed close to Sassy. Now and then the pony would thrust his muzzle down, sniffing at the dog, making sure, over and over, that his friend was still with him.

All the Tatums got a ride down into the valley with Tough Enough and Sassy. At last Pa stopped the truck in front of a stable next to the animal hospital. Beanie led the pony to a gate in a fence. He let down the gate's wooden bars and drew Sassy into a meadow beyond. Tough Enough trotted along beside him.

Beanie put the bars back. He turned to Sassy. "You rest here a spell and let the doctor medicine you up, then you'll be good as new."

Beanie saw puzzled wonder in the pony's soft eyes.

He watched him with a cold and hollow feeling in his stomach. He knew he would miss the pets he loved, he would miss them badly. But when he spoke to Sassy he did his best to make his voice firm and reassuring. "You'll like it here," he said. "You'll like it fine."

In spite of himself, sadness slipped into his voice. Tough Enough heard it. He whined. Sassy heard it, too, and he poked his nose into Beanie's neck. Beanie hugged him. "Now you go and get well real soon. We can't keep traipsin' down in the truck to visit with you. It's a far piece and gas costs a pretty penny."

Beanie squatted down and gave Tough Enough a squeeze. "You stay right here alongside of Sass so he won't get snorty and swivety," he said. "But I reckon I don't have to tell you that. And now—you two be good, you hear?"

Both animals watched him climb over the gate and into the truck. Sassy whinnied. He was too lame to paw at the gate. He sniffed at the narrow top bar with faint whooshing sounds. He mouthed it with his fleshy lips, he bit at it and shook it till it rattled. But he could not drag it down.

Tough Enough began to bark. He was begging Beanie not to leave him and Sassy behind. But the animals heard the truck start up; they saw it move away without them. Again and again Sassy whinnied. Now Tough Enough's barks were coming fast and frantic. The noise of the truck was dying away in the distance. It came fainter, still fainter, then it was only a rough thread of sound. A moment later they could no longer hear it.

The little dog never even thought of darting off after the truck and leaving Sassy behind. But as he stood looking up at the pony a shiver went through him, a whimper squeezed out of his throat. He could not understand what had happened. Beanie had always taken care of him and Sassy. He had fed them, petted them, talked to them and made them feel secure. Why had he left them behind in this strange meadow?

Tough Enough began to run; he went racing all around the grassy field. Was there a way out for the pony? If so, he meant to find it. But the fence was unbroken, he discovered. He scratched at the lowest bar of the gate, but it held fast.

He still had exploring to do, though. He went sniffing and peering all around the pasture to see if it was safe for his friend. Soon he was sure they were all alone.

He trotted back to Sassy. The two began to talk to each other, each in his own special way. A low, affectionate rumble sounded in Tough Enough's throat. Sassy was nickering softly. The pony lowered his muzzle and touched the dog's cool moist nose.

Close to the gate, Sassy started to graze in a halfhearted way. Tough Enough scratched absently, with an automatic foot, at the faint itch of an old flea bite. But their four alert ears were constantly turned toward the highway, listening for the wheeze-chug-rattle of the Tatum truck.

The two lingered near the gate till Jed came and led Sassy into the stable. Tough Enough trotted close behind. The doctor put Sassy into a stall and gave him oats for supper, and cool clear water. He ran a currycomb lightly over his coat and then a stiff brush; he rubbed him down with a soft clean cloth.

Next, he set a pan of dog food in front of Tough Enough, and a bowl of water. He looked down at the little dog—at his attentive, lifted ears, at his inquisitive eyes, at his coat of short sleek hair with black spots sprawling over clean white.

The doctor's humorous mouth quirked at a corner. "Reckon you're fit as a fiddle," he said to Tough Enough.

The dog whined eagerly. He stood up on his hind legs and pawed at the doctor's knee as if begging for help. The man bent down, smiling, and rubbed Tough Enough behind his ears. Then he went striding away toward his hospital.

The dog and the pony weren't hungry; they didn't eat much. They wanted, with a nagging sense of loss, to be back on the Tatum farm, back with Beanie. They had grown so used to the softness in his voice as he talked to them when he fed them, so used to the love in his hands as he patted and stroked them.

For Tough Enough, how variously pleasant it had been, to follow Beanie around the farm, watching him feed Pal, the old Tatum horse, trotting after him to the meadow—soft and richly sweet with a multitude of scents —when Beanie went to get the cows at milking time. Always, Tough Enough had to see what the other Tatum dogs were doing. It was fun to try stealing a bite or two of the big dogs' dinners, even though he always failed and got growled at. And the Tatum cats—it was fun to tease them and jump away from their reaching, scratching claws; fun to hear them spit at him in small, dry, breathy hisses; fun to see their affronted fluffed-out tails.

How different things were now. Unfamiliar smells in this stable made him long to fill his nose with Beanie's reassuring scent. Why didn't Beanie come for them?

Tough Enough lifted up his muzzle and howled. The pony lowered his head; his warm breath flowed down on the dog. For a comforting moment Tough Enough leaned against Sassy's foreleg, the leg that didn't hurt. Then he trotted away on a tour of the stable. It was empty, he found, except for another horse who kicked out at him when he came too close.

He went back to Sassy's stall. He turned around and around, flattening the hay on the floor under him until he had made a bed that would fit him. He lay down with his back to Sassy and to the wall, to be between the pony and any danger. Next, he laid his head across a paw and let out a long sighing breath. He drifted down into a shallow doze—a half-sleep he could quickly lift out of if suspicious sounds or smells should warn him.

During the night, between snatches of sleep, the dog and the pony heard noises out of the dark. The other horse in the stable began to wheeze. The wheezing changed to rasping as he tried to breathe. Soon his trouble eased. He was quiet.

Tremendous trucks went roaring by on the highway. Far away, a hound set up a baying clamor and waked all the dogs in the valley; for a while their barking came from far and near. Dogs in the hospital, close by, made a brief responding racket and even Tough Enough gave a yip.

The noises died down and ended, but every now and then, from the hospital, came the cry of a sick, lonesome animal. A puppy howled weakly, a cat meowed. Toward dawn a monkey gave a jungle screech.

That same morning, before the doctor left to care for his other patients, he examined Sassy's sore leg. He noticed a swelling below the knee. He felt unnatural warmth there. "Like I figured," he said to the pony, "you went and strained a tendon. All you need is a good long rest."

He let Tough Enough and Sassy out into the pasture. There they still kept their heads turned toward the highway. Their eyes and ears and noses were alert for

14

any sight or sound or smell that might tell them the Tatum truck was coming back.

Forlornly they kept poking around the meadow. Sassy worried at the top bar of the gate, biting it, grasping it in his gaping jaws and pulling. It bumped back and forth but stayed stubbornly in place.

Tough Enough went bounding off on one of his quick circuits of the pasture. When his new quest for freedom ended and he stopped beside the pony, his tail was drooping.

Time ambled along, sleepy and unexciting. The dreary day ended. Another dragged by, and another. Tough Enough's whole body, from tail tip to nose, showed his slackening spirits. His sadness was like a deep ache. Sassy no longer held his head high and proud.

In the meadow they had fallen into the same day-after-day routine. The pony would worry the top bar of the gate, then stand on three legs and doze. His coat would take the sun in glowing browns, and sudden little jerks would wrinkle it as he twitched flies away. The dog would trot off, again and again, on anxious circuits of the pasture, vainly seeking a break in the fence. Disheartened, every time, he would finally lie down close to his friend and soon he would be sleeping lightly. Often he would dream of the Tatum farm—dreams bright with remembered good times with Beanie and Beanie's brothers and sisters.

Now and then he would have a very different sort of dream, a kind of nightmare. It was always the same.

He would fancy he was sniffing the rank and dangerous smell of a long-ago wild boar, a great beast that had once come rushing after him, teeth bared, tusks gleaming. His tail would press close to his after end. The tip of his tremulous nose would twitch.

Then would come a keenly imagined chase: he in desperate flight, the wild boar in pursuit. Lying there on the pasture grass, he would utter faint dream whimpers and paw the air.

He would keep on dream twitching, dream whimpering and dream pawing until, in a climax of effort, he would jerk himself out of sleep, snorting a small startled "Hrrr-*uff.*" He would stare all around, out of still-apprehensive eyes, astonished to see no wild boar chasing him, no wild boar anywhere—just his friend Sassy standing near and the too-familiar meadow drowsing under a haze of summer heat.

One day, when Sassy was fussing and fretting at the top bar of the gate, shaking it back and forth, baffled anger rose in him. It drove him to try something new.

He began to pull the bar from side to side till he jerked an end off its support. Down went that end of the bar. It thudded against the ground. Now the gate was lower at one side—but could he leap over it?

The sudden sound pulled Tough Enough out of a

doze. He yipped. Then he bounded close to the pony, ears pricked forward. He knew what Sassy wanted; he wanted it, too. He whined. He cocked his head on one side. He was watching, listening, quivering.

The pony studied the bars that were still up. He turned and limped away from the gate, then he swung around, facing it. He broke into an awkward gallop, to get up speed, then he gathered his hindquarters together; his powerful leg muscles bulged; he gave a spring. Up he went, up and over the gate. He landed heavily on the other side. Sharp pain shot through his sore leg—but he was free! He rested until the pain dulled.

Tough Enough made himself low. He crawled under the fence and trotted up to the pony. The animals stood tense, waiting. Now what? Which way should they go? They scented the breeze as if it might give them an answer. Soon, with sure instinct, they turned toward the highway. They reached it and began to walk along it. They were moving toward the cove where the Tatum farm stretched its lofty acres—toward that little valley up in the Great Smoky Mountains. The pony's hoofs tapped-tapped the hard macadam; the dog's paw-nails made small clicking sounds.

Every now and then, Sassy would spread his nostrils and toss his head. Tough Enough's tail was up and waving. They were going home. They were sure of that.

2

A CAR came gliding up behind the dog and the pony. It drew closer and closer, then slowed and moved along a little way behind. The driver blew his horn again and again to get them off the road, but they would not turn aside.

The car slid still nearer. When Tough Enough saw its metal nose close by and heard the horn blaring into his large ears, he swerved. He nipped at one of the pony's heels and made him limp off onto the shoulder. The going was better there—the soft earth and grass were kinder to Sassy's hoofs.

More cars passed the animals. At last a truck came along. It slackened its forward thrust and kept pace with the dog and the pony. In a little while it passed them and went on ahead, but it was still moving slowly.

A man was driving, and a woman—his wife—was sitting next to him. When the man's shrewd gaze slid around to a place where the ground beyond the shoulder sloped up to a grassy bank, he pulled off the road. He drove along the shoulder, measuring the bank with an estimating squint, then stopped. There the bank was almost level with the floor of the truck, but it fell off sharply so he could back close to it.

The woman turned to the man. "Will Bumgarner, what you aimin' to do?" she asked.

"That there hoss is in trouble," the man said. "Bad trouble. Yep. And I'm fixin' to help him."

Will Bumgarner jumped down from the truck and went around behind it. He let down the tail gate, then he backed the truck until it touched the grassy bank.

When Sassy came limping up to the vehicle, Will moved slowly and carefully. He took hold of the pony's halter. His hand was gentle; Sassy let it stroke his nose. He kept a watchful eye on this stranger, but listened as Will talked kindly to him. The man had a way with animals, it seemed. Sassy pushed his muzzle against him.

Tough Enough sniffed at the overalls Will was wearing. He smelled so many different scrambled-up smells that his nose had trouble unscrambling them. The rank, heavy scent of skunk, the sharp scent of raccoon, of opossum, of fox, of bear, the scent of wild boar, pungent and menacing—all those were coming to him. He gave a growling bark. His hair stood up in a ridge along his back.

Will spoke to him gently and held out his hand. The dog nosed it; he got the man's own scent. He liked it. His high hair started to flatten. He let Will rub him behind the ears and as he felt the warmth of stroking fingers he wagged his tail a little.

The Tatums had taught Tough Enough and Sassy to obey; they had done it by being gentle and firm. Now the dog and the pony were ready to do this man's bidding because he was kind to them. So Sassy went along quite willingly as the man led him up the grassy bank and into the truck. The little dog trotted after them.

Will tied the end of a rope to Sassy's halter and made the other end fast to a wooden slat. That done, he moved the truck so he could put up the tail gate. Next, he eased the truck off the shoulder and back onto the road. He drove it along quite slowly, so the animals didn't get bumped or lose their footing when it went swinging around curves.

The woman broke a long silence. "I declare, Will Bumgarner, you look like a fox that knows where the henyard is! Are you a-helpin' that hoss or are you a-helpin' yourself to that hoss? Just answer me that."

"Shucks, Amanda, you know I wouldn't do nothin' wrong," the man said with a small sly grin. "That poor pony's in no shape to be traipsin' down the road. It was plumb pitiful to watch him. I'm just aimin' to give him a lift, like."

Amanda put her nose up. She sniffed. "What I'm afeared of is, you're aimin' to lift that hoss," she said.

"You know perfectly well he belongs to some folks around here. You'd best leave him be—him and that itty-bitty dog."

"Now, Amanda," said Will, "if I leave 'em be, it would be barefaced foolishment for sure. They'd just get 'emselves kilt dead by some speedin' fool, sure as shootin'. And that wouldn't do 'em or their owner no good nohow."

"Well," said Amanda, "let's us turn in at that farmhouse yonder and talk to the folks that live there. They'll maybe know whose hoss and dog they be."

"I'll do no such thing," said Will. "I don't know nothin' 'bout the folks round here in North Caroliny. They might say it was their hoss when it wasn't. They might sell that hoss to a glue factory or a cat-and-dog-food cannery; 'cause he's lame they might figure he ain't worth a June bug with a catbird after it."

"Will Bumgarner," Amanda said firmly, "the folks that own that hoss and that dog are bad worried about 'em right this minute, most likely. We'll pass a post office directly. Now you go in and tell the postmaster all about 'em. Put a notice up in there."

A corner of Will's mouth quirked in a smooth half-smile. "Now Amanda, I calculate the folks that own that little hoss don't know how to take good care of him. What do they go and do? They go and let him get lame, they don't cure him none, and they let him traipse all over the highway to get himself kilt by cars."

Will paused and gave Amanda a slanted, sidewise look. He went on once more: "Mighty triflin' folks and that's a true fact. They hadn't ought to have no animals nohow. I'm aimin' to take that little hoss home and cure him with that linament my grandpappy taught my pappy how to make, and my pappy taught me. Yep. It's plumb powerful stuff, I confidence it'll fix him up fine."

"Fiddle!" snorted Amanda. "Your grandpappy and your pappy used to say that linament would cure poison ivy, chigger bites, mange, cow pox, fallin' hair, measles *and* the itch. Now it stands to reason, a medicine supposed to cure *everything* won't cure *nothin'*."

Will gave a grunt almost like a growl. "Quit faultin' my grandpappy and my pappy," he said. "I've tried that linament on critters and it *worked*."

His wife looked at him in a soothing way. "Well, now," she said, "just as soon as you fix up that hoss or get all through a-tryin', you put a notice in the paper so the owner will see it and come get him."

"Sure, s-u-r-e." The man pulled the word out long and slick and slow. "Surest thing you know."

"Fiddlesticks!" said Amanda, sharply impatient again. "It *ain't* the surest thing I know. What about all them critters you let out o' traps and brought home? Folks is a-sayin' you're a-robbin' their traps."

"I'm tellin' you straight," said Will, "I don't give a snowball on a hot stove what they say. I just don't aim to stand by and see any animal suffer and not do nothin'

23

'bout it nohow. And you quit biddy-peckin' me! I declare, you been cluckin' and jabbin' at me till I'm plumb fit to be tied.''

"Great day in the mornin'!" said Amanda. "Kindness to dumb critters is one thing, stealin's another. You never pay me no mind. You'll find yourself in a lapful o' trouble one o' these days.''

Will frowned. Now his mouth looked like a turtle's, hard and down at the corners. "You done tongue-whup me enough," he said. He began to whistle, loud and harsh and tuneless.

In the back of the truck, Tough Enough was sniffing and poking around, growling out his anxious feelings. He had found a smell to worry about: a strong fox scent. But after thorough investigation he couldn't find any fox. He quieted. He sat down close to Sassy. He put his mind on scratching an itchy ear.

For a while, he and the pony rode along, fairly calm and contented. The truck was headed toward the Tatum farm; both were sure of that. Their deep direction sense told them.

The vehicle passed a narrow dirt road that led off the main highway, to the right. It was the steep twisting lane that went climbing up to the farm.

Tough Enough whimpered as the truck went thrusting on. Sassy pulled at the halter rope and whinnied. He stamped, once, on the truck's wooden floor, but the sudden jolt sent a twinge of pain up his lame leg. He did not stamp again.

On and on and on went the truck—up and down and up and down through the Great Smoky Mountains, over steep passes between high hills, down into a Tennessee valley. At last it stopped by a high stockade with a big sign in front of it, a sign that Will himself had lettered and stuck up. It said:

THE GREAT BUMGARNER ZOO
See the
WILDEST WILDCAT
See the
TERRIBLE WILD BOAR
See the
WORLD'S BIGGEST, MOST AWFULEST BEAR

Will had painted a giant wildcat. It was glaring over the fence in a steady, menacing way. Nearby, a huge painted snake—a python—writhed up and down along the top of the stockade.

During the many years that Will had owned the zoo, he had made it grow. Right from the start, Amanda had helped him. Looking after the animals wasn't much trouble, for long confinement in small cages had dulled their spirit.

Will and Amanda had been on their way home, after selling three young foxes to a zoo near Asheville, when Will had picked up Sassy and Tough Enough. Will hadn't wanted to part with the foxes, but he needed money to feed his many captive creatures.

Now he led the pony along the stockade and through a back door. Tough Enough followed at Sassy's heels. Inside, the animals looked around with nervous curiosity. They saw dozens of cages of different sizes with grass and shade trees between.

Their nostrils were full of strange animal scents. Sassy flung his head high and snorted. Tough Enough rumbled in his throat; he was filtering the air through his startled nose. Some of those pungent smells, he sensed, might mean danger to him and the pony.

One scent worried him more than any of the others; it seemed to carry the greatest threat. It lifted the hair along his spine. It put his ears back and stiffened out his tail, for it stirred memories of desperate flight and determined pursuit.

Will saw the sudden change in the dog and the pony. He talked to them in a soothing voice, doing his best to calm them.

When he began to lead the pony past one of the largest cages, Sassy reared and blew air out of his nose. Now Tough Enough was walking in a slow, tense, stiff-legged way. He started to bark loudly. There was the cage—the cage that most threatening smell was coming from.

He crept toward it, growling, his body low. As he

sniffed and looked and listened, he trembled. He pointed his nose toward the creature in a corner of the cage, an animal that seemed to be asleep. It was a wild boar. The great beast did not shift his body as the snarling dog crouched near. He just opened an eye, small and oddly red. Indifferent, he closed it again.

Tough Enough's snarls turned to quick lifting yips and yups. The dog was acutely puzzled. This boar looked and smelled like that other boar he had encountered a long time ago. But how different this motionless creature was, this quiet mass of flesh and bone and bristles—how unlike the fast, wiry, hot-tempered hog that had once chased him through the woods.

Little by little, Tough Enough grew aware that this caged creature would not even try to burst out and attack. His yapping thinned out and stopped. He gave a low asking whine, a sort of postscript.

Will led the pony on again. He had a struggle, pulling him past a cage with a black bear inside it. The bear *was* large, but certainly not "the world's biggest." And far from being "the most awfulest," it looked no more awful than a great heap of black car robes tossed into the cage. Like the boar, it was stretched out asleep in the mid-day warmth.

Farther along, they passed another cage. Behind its bars a wildcat looked down at them from the branch of an old tree set into the cage's concrete floor. The big cat

yawned, flattening its ears, moving its whiskers forward. It turned listless eyes on the dog and the pony.

Tough Enough checked a bark that had started in his throat; all that came out of him was a scratchy rasping.

Will guided him and Sassy past a skunk, a raccoon, an opossum—past a fox, some rabbits and a lonesome hawk. The dog sensed something different, something odd about all of them. They were not like wild creatures running free or flying overhead. His eyes and ears and nose told him they lacked spirit. But he was still aware that this strange place would have to be carefully looked over and completely sniffed at before he could be sure it was safe for him and the pony.

Will brought the two animals to an old shed. He tied the end of Sassy's halter rope to a doorpost. Then, to make room for the pony, he pushed out an old wheelbarrow and a rusty lawnmower. He drew Sassy inside the shed. That done, he looked down at Tough Enough, his humorous eyes half shut. "No need to tie you up, I reckon," he said. "If I know you, you feisty itty-bitty dog, you'll stick to that lame pony till hens give milk and cows lay eggs."

Will put a big pot on the stove in a cottage near the zoo, the simple cottage where he and Amanda lived. He filled the pot full of the linament his grandfather and his father used to make.

Every morning and every evening, Will would heat

up the thick brown mixture until it began to steam. Each time it had cooled off enough, he would soak a cloth in it, wring it out, and rub it over Sassy's lame leg. In spite of what Amanda had said, the linament made Sassy's leg feel better. After each treatment the pony would give Will a grateful nose nudge.

It wasn't long before Will saw that Sassy and Tough Enough had grown accustomed to their new home. He untied the rope so the pony could roam around the fenced-in lot. He knew that either he or Amanda would always be in there to keep an eye on both animals.

Free to move around, the pony and the dog began to search for a way out. But the stockade was solid; all exits were bolted against them. Tough Enough stood up on his hind legs and scratched at the back door where they had come in, then he dropped down and put his nose close to the crack under it. He whimpered. He threw his weight—all of his fifteen pounds—against it. But it held fast.

The pony poked his muzzle against the doorknob. He covered it wetly with his flexible lips. They pulled and they pushed at it, testing, fumbling around. He opened his mouth, to take it in his teeth, but Will gave him a mild slap on his flank and made him go away.

3

DURING the days that followed, tourists kept coming in to see the zoo. Amanda would sell them tickets at the front gate, then Will would take them around and tell them about the animals.

Once a little girl petted Sassy and wanted to ride him. But Will told her the pony had a lame leg and no one was allowed to get up on his back.

Will had another sick creature to care for—a baby rooster. It had had pneumonia, but it was getting well.

Many days before, it had wandered away from the mother hen and caught cold on a rainy night. Will had lifted it, half drowned, out of a ditch and had brought it home.

"Gracious sakes alive!" Amanda had said. "Where did you find that poor little comin'-to-pieces critter? Whose biddy is it, anyhow?"

Will had said he didn't know; it had been raining so hard, and was so dark, he hadn't had any notion where he was; he hadn't seen a thing.

Amanda sniffed. "Humph!" she said. "A likely story. Not so dark you couldn't see an itty-bitty chick!"

Will's lips didn't answer, but his hands did. They went to work, trying to save the young rooster, gently rubbing mustard salve into its skin.

Tough Enough knew all about the small, sick bird. He had sniffed it out, after Amanda had wrapped it in a bit of blanket and put it in a shoe box where it fitted snugly. Touching the bird with his nose, he had given a sort of half bark, polite and pleased but questioning. His tail had wagged a little.

The small rooster didn't respond. It lay quiet, hot with fever. Tough Enough's sensitive ears could hear it wheezing faintly as it breathed.

It got well faster than Sassy did. One morning it squirmed out of the tiny blanket and hopped right out of the box. The salve had helped, but it had burned away the chick's feathery down and had darkened and toughened its tender skin. For a time, no feathers grew on it.

Will called it Hallelujah Barebones, the nickname of a poor little scrawny mountain preacher he had known. Hallelujah followed him all around the fenced enclosure, whenever he fed the animals. Every time he sat down it would flap its wings and squawk and do its best to jump up on his lap.

Each night, it snuggled up to Tough Enough. Each day, except at feeding times, it stayed very close to him.

It hopped up on his back or on his head whenever he lay down. Sometimes its small claws felt scratchy, but Tough Enough was patient; he never shook it off.

Slowly, very slowly, the pony was getting better. He was using his right leg more and more.

"Reckon the hot sun down here is doin' him as much good as anything," said Amanda.

Little by little he stopped limping. Then Will began to let children—one at a time—ride around the zoo on Sassy's back. Tough Enough would trot after the pony, and Hallelujah Barebones, squawking and flapping and stepping fast, would follow Tough Enough. Children in the enclosure would stop looking at the other animals and watch and giggle and shout. The dog would cock his ears and spread his mouth in a sort of grin and swing his flattered tail.

For him and the pony, those hours of amusing children were the only bright hours of each day. The rest of the time they still longed to be back with Beanie, back on the Tatum farm.

One morning, Amanda asked Will when he was going to put a notice in the paper—a notice about the dog and the pony, so the people who owned them would know where they were and come for them.

Will said slowly, "Well-l-l, I reckon I'll wait a spell. I've put a slew o' hay and oats and such into this little hayburner and a heap o' meat into this itty-bitty dog.

Yep, I have. Hay and oats and dog food set me back plenty, and that linament cost money to make, and an ad in the paper wouldn't be for free, neither, nohow. I only git ten cents for a ride on the pony. So I figure I'll let these critters work a while to pay me back for what I've put in their stummicks and all."

Amanda eyed him steadily. "Them two animals don't eat much and you know it," she said. "They eat enough to stay alive, but not much more. I reckon they're mighty homesick."

"Well, they got a good home right here with us," Will insisted.

Amanda shook her head at him. "Will, you're plumb daft about critters, always hankerin' after 'em. Once you latch on to one you hate to part with it." She made her mouth thin.

More and more people brought children to the Bumgarner Zoo. Amanda made a dress and a sunbonnet for Hallelujah Barebones. Will was delighted. "Don't that beat all!" he exclaimed.

Amanda said, "That rooster biddy was plumb piti-ful, but now it's more perked up, like."

The children loved the dressed-up chicken, so Will asked his wife to make some clothes for Tough Enough and Sassy.

"Heavenly day!" she exclaimed. "I know you, Will Bumgarner. That hoss has a brand on him and that dog has some special markin's and spots his owner would know, right off. So you're hankerin' to hide that dog and that hoss under clothes so their folks won't know 'em, happen they come this way."

Will's answer came in a voice as smooth as cream. "Now, Amanda, that notion never crossed my mind. It plumb tickles me to pieces to make young-uns happy, you know that. They love that dressed-up biddy—the way you fancied it up is right cute—and they'd dote on a dressed-up dog and a hoss with clothes on him."

Amanda sniffed. "I know your tricks and your manners." But she thought to herself that maybe the dressed-up animals would bring more people and more money, so Will could pay for a notice in the paper.

So, for Tough Enough, she made a dress out of an old tablecloth and a blond wig out of frayed rope. And from her clever fingers, busy on some old flowered cretonne curtains, came two pairs of trousers and a jacket for Sassy.

Will gave her a battered straw hat of his, for the pony. She cut two holes in it, so his ears could poke through.

They had a difficult time, getting the clothes on the animals. And, once they had them on, it was even harder to keep them on. Both the dog and the pony hated their costumes, at first. They bit and scraped at them, trying to tear them off. But Will and Amanda were patient.

Whenever the animals stopped worrying at their clothes, the zoo man and his wife petted them and gave Sassy a carrot and Tough Enough a morsel of meat. Finally the pony and the dog, eager for tidbits and attention, stopped struggling.

Amanda and Will put the clothes on them only when visitors came. Will trained the dog to lead the pony around the enclosure by a long red ribbon. One end was tied around the pony's nose, the other was attached to Tough Enough's collar. Hallelujah Barebones would follow behind, always perky, always stepping with a strut.

Will laughed. "Ain't that the beatin'est thing?"

He made a new sign and stuck it up outside, by the other one. It said:

NEW ATTRACSHUN

It's Funny! It's Different! It's Astonishing!

SEE THE LITTLE LADY LEAD THE BIG MAN AROUND

BY THE NOSE

Children and grown-ups, too, made such a fuss over Tough Enough and Sassy that the little dog got keen, wagging satisfaction out of doing his trick. Sassy accepted the routine cheerfully. After each performance Will gave the pony a bit of apple or carrot and rewarded the dog with a little piece of meat.

"I declare," Will said to Amanda, "they're mighty smart, real circus critters, dogged if they ain't."

Amanda said, "They've made enough money now, I reckon. When are you goin' to let their folks know where they be?"

Will shook his head in sorrow. "Be a shame to put eddicated critters like these back on some no-account hillbilly farm. Yep, it would. A downright crime to make that little high-toned hoss do heavy farm work."

Amanda gave a sigh. "Just what I was afeared of, all along." She said nothing more.

4

THE HOURS turned into days, the days into weeks. Tough Enough and Sassy were beginning to forget about the Tatum farm. Even memories of Beanie were starting to grow dim.

One afternoon the animals inside the stockade grew restless; they were tense, listening, waiting. From time to time, Sassy would throw up his head and snort, to clear his nostrils, and then sniff the air, to test it. Tough Enough had his tail down. Now and then he whimpered softly.

Amanda took the costumes off the dog and the pony, since they were in no mood for tricks.

"Wonder what's bitin' 'em all?" one of the visitors asked Will.

"Reckon there's a storm a-brewin'," Will said glumly.

Amanda turned her eyes up to the sky. It had a strange, brassy look, but it was still clear. "Nary a cloud anywheres," she said.

Tough Enough lifted his nose. He gave a howl: long, plaintive, almost wolf-like. Hallelujah Barebones, in Sassy's shed, perched on a board, hunched up, immobile.

Will shook his head. "Critters know," he said. "Yep, they know a heap."

Far away, a windstorm was moving across the sultry Tennessee valley, bringing a torrent of cool air, sweeping along toward the zoo. It was making small waves on a brook beside a road, stirring up red-brown whirls of dust, dead leaves, twigs, scraps of paper. Spreading strange darkness as it came, it was gathering force, blustering onward, flattening fields of corn, pushing at trees, tossing and breaking their branches, bending their tormented trunks.

When ragged clouds started to sweep the sky over the zoo, visitors began to leave in a nervous hurry, hoping to drive home before the storm could break. When all of them had gone, Will and Amanda ran to shut the windows in their cottage.

Sassy was standing still, ears pricked forward. He jerked his head up and gave a snort of alarm. The caged animals were pacing back and forth, back and forth. In the woods outside the enclosure, frightened birds were making strange little moaning sounds.

All of a sudden the storm struck the zoo. It was like an oncoming wall, a great swift wall of wind. Mingling with its roar were shrill whinings overhead.

A clothesline with laundry clinging to it went whipping over the zoo. In its wake, spinning wildly, a great limb of a tree came sweeping. A tin roof, torn from a house, sailed by.

Out of the throats of caged animals, frightened sounds were coming: huffings and snortings from the bear, whines from the fox, hoarse squeals from the boar and from the raccoon a queer quavering as it pulled at its ruff and its whiskers with slim black fidgety fingers. But the creatures in cages had more protection than Tough Enough and Sassy. Bits of flying debris missed the dog and the pony by inches.

The boards of the stockade were creaking sharply, starting to lean with the mighty wind. Great gusts sent sinewy fingers to feel out weak spots in the wood.

The tumult of the storm grew louder. A shrill blast picked up a tool shed outside and slammed it against the fence with such force that the shed splintered and fell apart. Screaming in terror, Sassy reared, stood for a moment on trembling legs, then dropped down on all fours. He wheeled. He galloped about in panic, hoofs thudding. Tough Enough ran after him, barking, nipping at his heels, trying to make him stop his senseless racing around.

A violent gust went driving into boards the tool shed had battered. The weakened wood snapped and splintered. Boards, hurtling across the enclosure, threw themselves against the far side, each striking with a crash.

No creatures were near enough to be hit by flying planks.

The pony was almost exhausted. His wild galloping slowed to a canter; he stopped, half dazed, oddly subdued. With well-aimed nips, Tough Enough sent him to a corner of the enclosure; he persuaded him to stand there.

Now the pony and the dog were on the sheltered side of the stockade, some distance from the break. The fence gave some protection. They were out of the storm's full force.

Sassy's eyes were still big with fear; his distended nostrils quivered. Tough Enough kept watch on him, ready to head him off if he should start to bolt.

When, at last, there was a slight lull in the storm, the dog saw his chance. He urged the pony across the enclosure, to the broken gap in the fence. He nipped at his heels to drive him through the opening, then followed not far behind.

Now they found themselves in a wide, level field. There the wind had a clear sweep. Even though it had slackened a little, flying sand and pebbles cut the animals' skin. They found it hard to breathe. Moving slowly, pushing against the rush of air, they struggled along.

Before the storm could gather full force again, the dog saw a deep gully; he urged the pony along till both of them were down in its shelter.

Sassy's sides were heaving. He stood shivering, fretting. Tough Enough ran round and round him, poking him with his nose and paws and now and then licking a leg.

The storm regained part of its power, then rapidly lost strength. Before it had fully spent itself, and while the sky was still quite dark, Tough Enough and Sassy left their shelter. Both were bewildered, but determined to get away from a place where such things could happen. They went wandering across the windswept field, then into a forested region.

Cautiously Sassy picked his way over fallen trees and branches, with the dog leading him on by jumping over them. Then they zigzagged across a stretch of treeless country. The pony was moving vaguely behind the ir-resolute dog. Neither knew where to go, except to keep pushing on. They were free, but they did not know what to do with their sudden freedom.

The setting sun burst through tattered clouds. Little by little the wind died down. The quiet calmed the ani-mals. They stopped their aimless wandering. They rested.

Out of the stillness came a sound, very faint and pure: the piping of a tired white-throated sparrow. Both the dog and the pony had listened to those same clear notes, back on the Tatum farm. In both, memories stirred and grew stronger. Memories of safety. Memories of contentment.

Sassy put his ears forward; he fixed his eyes on the

distance, turning and turning his head. His nostrils quivered; he spread them wide, sniffing a new breeze as if it were telling him things. His muscles tightened. His aimlessness was gone; now, once more, he had a purpose. He snorted and arched his neck. Then he whirled and started off at an easy flowing gallop, heading eastward toward a distant stand of hemlocks. Tough Enough raced after him, yipping. He, too, knew where they were going. The deep homing instinct in both of them was sending them toward the Great Smokies, mountains not yet in view. Their massive domes and ridges lay far beyond the blue-gray hills, fold behind fold, ahead.

Once the dog stopped. He swung around and looked back, with one foot lifted a little. The tip of his tongue came out and ran around a corner of his mouth. This was supper time—the time of day when Will Bumgarner had fed him and Sassy. But he turned sharply and gazed at the pony, still galloping along. He gave some short barks, loud and resolute. He went bounding after Sassy.

5

A FEW DAYS after the storm, a truck pulled up outside Will Bumgarner's zoo. It was the old Tatum truck. First Beanie and then Pa Tatum jumped out. Climbing over boards and debris that high winds had tossed around, they made their way toward the small structure at the entrance. It was leaning at a crazy angle. They went inside. No one was there, but they could hear a hammering, beyond.

Pa pushed a hip against a turnstile. It moved. He and Beanie went through and found themselves inside the enclosure.

Will Bumgarner was hammering a board in place by the break in the stockade. He had a large white bandage around his head. Near him, a young rooster, scrawny and rather bedraggled, was stepping around with an aimless, dispirited air.

Pa went up to Will. "Mornin'," he said.

Will put his hammer down. He said, "Mornin'."

"Tatum's my name," said Pa. "This here's my son, Beanie."

"I'm Will Bumgarner," said Will. "Glad to meet you folks."

"We live in Sourwood Cove," Pa went on, "Hemphill Valley, Haywood County, North Caroliny. I run a farm there....Looks like you had a mess o' trouble here."

"Yep, that's a fact," said Will. "We sure did, a heap o' trouble. A big wind come a-roarin' up and *wham* it flattened us out—yep, it did."

"Sure am sorry," Pa said. "We don't aim to bother you none at a time like this. We'd just like to ask you a question or two and then we'll be a-moseyin' along."

"Fire away," said Will. "No trouble, no trouble a-tall. Stay as long as you like."

"Much obliged," said Pa. "Well, my son Beanie here had a dog and a pony. Pony was lame...."

Will stiffened. Pa had been watching him intently, and now his eyes narrowed. He stopped talking, then began again, drawling but drily distinct. He was telling about taking Sassy and Tough Enough to the animal hospital.

His words came faster as he went on from there: "But them two, they broke plumb out o' the pasture and lit out. We hunted high and low for that itty-bitty dog and that limpin' pony, but we couldn't find hide nor hair of 'em, anywheres. We was mighty down in the mouth. I put a piece in our neighborhood paper, too— kept it in till my money pretty nigh ran out. That hoss and that dog mean a sight to Beanie, here. They mean a sight to all us Tatums."

Will shifted his weight from one foot to another. He was frowning. He looked away from Pa and Beanie.

"Some folks in Maggie Valley near us run a zoo like yours," Pa went on. "They heard tourist folks a-talkin' 'bout a zoo in Tennessee with a pint-sized dog and a pony. They knew we'd lost a dog and a pony so they told us mebbe they was in Tennessee."

Pa stopped. There was a heavy silence.

At last Will spoke. "Folks, I done wrong. I wronged you-all, yep I did. I was the one saw that sweet little pony a-limpin' along the highway and that feisty, itty-bitty dog a-lookin' after him so good and careful, just a-hangin' on to him like one of his own fleas."

Beanie was squirming with excitement. He kept his eyes on Will's face as Will went on: "My heart, it plumb turned over, them two was so pitiful, like. And I was real cross to think folks would treat poor dumb critters that-a-way. I didn't know the true facts—no, I didn't. I just figured them two critters was mistreated, so I picked 'em up in my truck."

Now Beanie's eyes were wide with joy. "Oh, mister, you found 'em!" he cried. He looked all around the enclosure, but he saw only the caged animals. "Where are they?" he asked.

Will swallowed hard.

"Yes, where be they?" Pa's voice had an edge on it.

Will looked at Pa and then at Beanie. At last he brought out, "Folks, I'm mighty sorry. I don't rightly know where they be."

Beanie went cold inside. He blinked back sudden stinging tears.

Pa was scowling at Will. He clenched his fists. "Keep talkin', man," he said.

So Will began to tell them about the storm. Soon he was saying, "It done tore the roof off our house and my old woman got her arm busted and I got a bad cut in my head, real bad. After the doc come and fixed us up, I hunted everywhere for that dog and that pony till I was plumb tired in my bones—but I couldn't find 'em. I asked everybody round here, but nobody had seen 'em, they was all too shook up by the storm, I reckon. The roads was blocked and wires was down. It was hard to get around to see folks and ask about the critters. But I cured your hoss of his lameness. Yep, I did." Will's eyes had a pleading look in them. "I done that for you-all, anyhow; I done it with my grandpappy's linament."

"Mebbe so." Pa's voice held so much hatred that Beanie was startled and a little scared. He hardly knew this man beside him.

"Reckon you're nothin' but a low-down hoss thief," Pa said in a forced, half-choked voice.

Will was looking down at the ground. When he

spoke, his voice was low and dragging. "I'm powerful sorry for what I done. It'll stay with me, the way a heap of other bad things have stayed....My life ain't been much more than climbin' out o' mistakes."

There was silence for a time. Then Pa put his hand on Beanie's shoulder. "Let's us go, son," was all he said.

They left Will standing there with his hands hanging limp and his shoulders hunched over. They climbed into the truck. Soon they were rattling and chug-chugging back toward the Tatum farm.

6

TOUGH ENOUGH and Sassy were moving toward the Tatum farm, too, but much more slowly and in fields far from the highway. It was good, so very good, not to be shut up inside a stockade. Every now and then the pony would prance and snort and toss his head. He would gallop for a while, his coat shining in the sun, his tail, a tawny gold, floating along the wind.

Tough Enough, running in spurts to keep up with him, would leap and caper like a puppy, his wet tongue hanging out, feeling cool in the breeze of his speed. Once, just for fun, he chased a dragonfly, its glossy wings ablaze in the sun. It zigzagged, then darted off like a bullet.

His nose was savoring familiar deep-country smells: the rich earth scent, the fragrance of flowers, the pungency of weeds. But, as he and the pony crossed a highway, he sneezed as his nose sucked in the lingering sour smell of gasoline.

Whenever the pony stopped the dog would stop, too. Sometimes Tough Enough would dig in fertile soil,

poking his nose deep in and sniffing earnestly before he pulled it out, plastered over at its tip with damp brown earth.

Both were finding happiness in roaming through sun-warmed, sweet-scented brush, in drinking from cold, rushing brooks, in hearing the steady whisper of water over rocks, in splashing and swimming in clear ponds.

At night, it was good to feel the cool breath of the earth—good to be out when stars shone down softly through a tender haze, out among the dry rustlings of late summer and the incessant rattlings and sawings of insects.

Sometimes a bat would swoop close with a sweep of small dark wings and a faint fanning of air. Now and then a distant fox would bark, sharp and clear, and always crickets chirped and fireflies sparkled against the thick darkness of pines.

Rain came down. It felt cool and cleansing. On stretches bare of grass the dust drank up the first few drops, but as they fell faster it turned to twinkling mud, soft under paws and hoofs.

When the clouds parted and the sun blazed out, wet diamonds sparkled on washed leaves and bracken. Rich scents filled the air. As two noses sucked them in, Tough Enough sneezed with sheer pleasure.

Sometimes fog would close in around the pair. It felt cool and damp in their noses and throats; it clung to their coats in moist beads. In the dense, drifting clouds they found it hard to see the narrow animal trails they were following.

Deep in stands of trees, squirrels scolded them. Shy, hidden birds stopped singing as they drew near, and then began again when they had passed.

Sassy was getting enough to eat; his green dinner was waiting, below, almost every time he lowered his nose. But it was not easy for Tough Enough to find food. He had grown accustomed to Beanie's setting out suppers for him. Jed, the animal doctor, and then Will Bumgarner had fed him well every night. Now he was on his own.

His hopeful nose would sniff around. A fat blundering beetle, now and then, or an unwary grasshopper was hardly filling. The middle of him felt hollow; there was a gnawing inside it and now and then a twisting. Hunger sharpened his instincts, quickened all his senses. He learned by trial and error to become a hunter.

Whenever a breeze came blowing toward him he would grow keenly aware. If it brought him exciting news of something to eat, he would stop and sniff, nose thrust forward, tail rigid and level like a pointer's. Then he would crouch and creep toward the scent that tingled in his greedy nose. No hunting cat could have been more slyly careful.

He would ease his body along the smell that lay across the ground, ever thicker and warmer. And then—

the sudden final leap which might bring a small rabbit or mouse or squirrel into his jaws—or might not. He could never tell. But with constant practice he did better. As raw meat went into his body, most of his weakness left him. He could keep going.

He had to leave Sassy whenever he went hunting, but the animals understood each other's needs. The pony would crop tufts of wavy grass, his only sudden movements the swishings of his tail to drive away pestering flies. Whenever the dog would come back, the pony would nicker a welcome and Tough Enough's throat would rumble gently.

Now and then they traveled over land scorched by fire—sun-soaked open country where blackberry bushes, thistles, Queen Anne's lace and black-eyed Susans had taken root.

Once, three yelling boys chased them. The dog and the pony took to their heels. Sassy's hoofs clinked and clattered on stones and bare juttings of rock as the two left the boys far behind.

Another time, they wandered into a steep cornfield on a mountain farm. The green stalks rustled in a breeze; they made a gentle sound. But suddenly the roar of a shotgun tore the air to shreds. Bird shot stung Sassy's flanks, burned Tough Enough's skin. A farmer had fired at them from his cabin porch.

Terrified, they fled. The pony—eyes wide, nostrils

flaring—took low bushes in stride and leaped over higher ones. The dog, tail tucked as far between his legs as he could make it go, raced along in a frenzy of motion, zigzagging when he had to, doing his utmost to keep up. They did not stop to rest till the cornfield lay a long distance behind.

After that they were careful to stay away from people. They traveled mostly at night.

One evening they came to the wide waters of a lake they could not swim across; they had to plod part way around it, anxiously skirting the shore. Now and then a high fence barred their way and sent them off on a tiresome detour.

Little by little, as the two traveled eastward, an odd change began to come over the countryside. Hemlocks and oaks and pines were growing sparse and stunted. The dog and the pony passed fewer and fewer trees until, at last, there were none; coarse grasses and pokeweed had taken over.

As they pushed on and on, the poke clumps, too, shrank and vanished. Springs dried up. The grasses thinned out, gave way to desolate ground with just a small patch of vegetation dotting it here and there.

Sassy stopped and nibbled at a lonesome clump of clover, withered and brown. All around the animals, gaunt, barren slopes—orange-red nearby, a rosy amethyst in the distance—lay scorched under a downpour of sun.

A small hot wind eddied across gullies carved deep in raw clay.

The two, in their homeward course, had come into a strange region: the Great Copper Basin in the southeast corner of Tennessee. It was a long and lonesome stretch of land laid waste by copper smelting a great many years before. First had come reckless tree-cutting to fuel greedy furnaces, then drifting sulphur fumes from smelters had stifled all remaining green things.

The little dog whimpered. He lifted his head; his nostrils sampled the air. He was hoping to catch a scent from some place where green life still lingered. He smelled nothing but earth baked hard and dry—no scent of any living thing.

Once he and Sassy heard the creaky cry of a solitary starling; once a locust gave a plaintive chirp—then silence shut down again.

They kept plodding through the heat, their heads low. Sweat was pouring off Sassy. Tough Enough's tongue was hanging out; his sides heaved as he panted. The red clay felt burning hot against the pads of his paws.

Soon both were near exhaustion. But they drove themselves across dry creek beds, up and down the steep slopes of gullies, along the tops of sun-baked ridges. Beyond this frightening desert, instinct told them, lay the farm. Their homeward urge was stronger than ever; they could not turn aside, could not go back, could not stop.

On and on they pushed, up to higher ground. A breeze fanned them gently; their lungs drew it in gratefully. It was making slow silvery ripples across the leaves of a solitary kudzu vine that had managed to take root and grow.

Sassy threw his head high. He thrust his ears forward; he widened his nostrils, scenting the little wind. All of a sudden he snorted. A new vigor filled him. He began to trot.

Tough Enough gave a yip. He ran forward, eyes alert, nose working. Now he and the pony were sniffing an exciting scent. It came from a slope ahead: the smell of grass! With its freshness in their noses they drove themselves along.

At last they reached an upward stretch where scattered spears of green had pushed up through hard soil. Farther on, the earth was softer, darker, richer; there the blades grew thick and juicy. The pony lowered his nose impatiently. He cropped up succulent mouthfuls. He lay down, rolled over and over, then heaved himself up and stood, breathing the good air deeply.

The tired dog stretched himself out with his head between his paws. He felt the grass, soft and cool, against his stomach. He heard the crooning of bees, the whisper of a breeze drawing slow fingers through bushes. He lay there for a long time. Little by little, new hope came to him.

Ruth Carroll

Sassy was growing restless. He shook his head. He whinnied. Slowly, looking back at the dog, he started off. Tough Enough got up and followed.

As they moved along, small hemlocks began to dot the countryside, then little oaks and spruces. The trees increased in number and in size. Finally the animals were pushing through a thick wood.

They found a stream and drank with noisy slurpings. Farther along the watercourse they reached a deep pool. Both plunged in and came out dripping. The pony pranced and, for a moment, stood up on his hind legs, his forelegs pawing the air. The dog shook himself from nose to tail, sending off a shower of glittering drops.

Suddenly he went rigid, staring down. Something in motion under the surface had caught his eyes; something greenish with legs and claws and a tail. It was a crawfish—a creature that looked like a small lobster—hurrying toward a hole under a sunken rock.

The dog dived in. He seized the crawfish by the tail and carried it out on the bank. There he ate it in a crunching hurry, tilting his head, half shutting his eyes, savoring every bite.

With new strength in them, the two went on and on—up through a stony mountain pass, down into a wooded valley.

A breeze brought Tough Enough's nose a message: the exuberant message that food more filling than a crawfish was not far away. How well he knew those scents: *Ham. Cornbread. Chocolate cake.* Quick wetness filled his mouth.

Off he started toward those splendid smells, leaving the pony grazing beside a brook. His skilled nose led him along. It took him to the edge of a grassy clearing where a family—a mother and a father and seven children—were going to have a picnic, later on. Around that open place tall ferns grew thick.

The dog stood up on his hind legs and poked his muzzle through a spreading spray of ferns. Now he could see the people. He was afraid of them, but hunger made him bold. They did not notice a small black sniffing nose and two eager brown eyes, for they were hard at work. They were searching for precious stones: rubies and sapphires. This was a region rich in surface minerals waiting to be mined.

Visitors who liked to hunt for gems—"rock hounds" they called themselves—would pay the owners of these acres for permission to mine there. With pickaxes they would dig up dark topsoil and the putty-colored clay underneath. They would shovel the clay into pails and carry it to nearby streams. There they would empty it into "screens"—contrivances of metal mesh set in wooden frames—and let clear water flow through it, tilting the screens first one way and then the other so the current would wash the mud and sand away and leave nothing but a layer of stones. Then they would peer and pick among the stones for any that might have value.

That was what this family was doing. While all nine of them labored in the creek bed, each calling out to the others whenever he found a hopeful-looking stone, Tough Enough had found their big basket of food. Tantalizing smells—the ham smell was the most enticing—drove him almost wild. He felt a convulsive twisting in his middle. His nose skimmed over the basket with quick exploring sniffs, then it went poking deep in.

Almost at once he found it: the great ham his nose had announced. He bit into it deeply. Its crust was sweet with juices of pineapple and orange. Trembling, he dragged it out. He began to tear at it and wolf down tender chunks.

At last the mother happened to glance around. She saw him. "Look what that dog's *doing!*" she screamed.

She and the rest of the family forgot about gems. They all began to shout at Tough Enough, but he got a firm hold on what was left of the ham and started to run. The mother and the children picked up stones and threw them; the father found a stick and started after him.

A sharp stone struck the dog's right side. He yelped and let go of the ham. He kept on running fast in spite of pain; he went racing to a rhododendron thicket and began to force his way deep in. The people couldn't follow him there.

When they were out of sight and their faraway shouting came faintly, the dog stopped and stood panting. He licked a deep cut in his side. Slowly he made his way out of the dense green tangle, then started to struggle back to Sassy. The distance was short but it seemed cruelly long. At last, with a whine, he dropped down beside the pony.

Sassy thrust his ears forward. He whinnied. He lowered his head and nosed the dog gently, seeming to understand that Tough Enough was hurt. He stood over him protectively, looking down from time to time out of large grave eyes.

Next day, it was hard for the dog to move. His side was stiff. He was hot with fever. But he crawled to the stream and lapped up water eagerly, then lay down nearby.

Stepping slowly and carefully, the pony walked over to him. He lowered his muzzle and blew his warm breath down. The little dog raised his head; he and Sassy touched noses. Tough Enough's tail moved weakly.

The following morning the fever was almost gone. Tough Enough staggered to his feet and began to walk uncertainly. Once more he drank from the stream, then tried feebly to hunt for food. He found the remains of a chicken sandwich some tourist had tossed aside, and part of a hard-boiled egg. He snapped them up. Now he felt a little stronger.

At dusk, the next day, he and Sassy began to move slowly toward the still-distant Tatum farm.

After a while, though quite unaware of it, they crossed a boundary. Now they were in the Great Smoky Mountains National Park. Vast numbers of wild creatures had taken refuge in its abundant forests. Once there, they had found they were safe from Man; it was against the law for him to set his hand against any living thing.

The Park animals were practiced at finding food, some feeding on vegetation, some on one another. They were skilled at sniffing out scraps that tourists had neglected to put in garbage cans with firm-fitting lids, the cans that rangers had set at intervals along the roads and in the camping grounds. In spite of so much competition, Tough Enough nosed out some picnic leavings and wolfed them down. But it grew increasingly hard for him to find anything. Almost always, if food lay on the forest floor, other animals had gotten there first.

The hungry hours dragged on, each one grimly the same. The little dog grew desperate.

One night his nose picked up a message. People again. People not far away. He and Sassy were resting near a camp ground.

Driven by hunger and hope, Tough Enough left Sassy. The pony opened an eye, gave a gentle asking nicker, and then slipped back to the edge of sleep.

Moving slowly and with stealth, Tough Enough made his way toward the camp. Other creatures were hunting there while the campers slept. A family of skunks was poking around, finding a scrap here, a crumb there, by one of the outdoor fireplaces. At the edge of the river nearby, a raccoon was washing an apple core before eating it; he was turning it round and round in an absent-minded way.

Tough Enough reached the edge of the camp grounds and paused, looking at a cluster of tents and cars and trailers there, keyed up for warnings of danger.

Venturing forward once more, he began to move back and forth, keeping well away from the skunks and the raccoon. On and on he went in earnest zigzags, trying to skim every inch of ground with the tip of his nose. Finally he knew that further search would be useless. A scrap of sausage meat and a bitten-into cookie—those were all he had found.

Disheartened, he made his way back to the pony. He lay down. When sleep came to him, it was shallow and restless.

At dawn he was up and moving around. He drank at the brink of the river, then stole close to the camp tents and trailers. When he heard muffled sounds from inside a tent he went trotting up to the top of a little hill.

There he lay down at the edge of a patch of mountain laurel, a strategic spot where he could see out, yet not be seen. From this hiding place he began to spy on the camp, his eyes intent, his well-licked nose alert.

In late afternoon a beautiful smell came wandering his way—the scent of steak. His nose sucked and sucked it in.

A boy was carrying the steak. He laid it on the metal bars of an outdoor grill, over a slow fire of glowing embers. Then he stepped back inside a tent. Another boy went walking off, carrying a pail.

Tough Enough's muzzle thrust forward; his tail went straight and stiff and level. All of him, from nose to tail tip, was aiming itself at that steak. He crept toward it, along and along, then suddenly he made a rush.

When he got near, the heat of red embers stopped him, for he was afraid of fire, but the smell of sizzling meat tantalized his nostrils. Saliva came flooding into his mouth. He licked his nose again and again, wiggling and wiggling it.

His hunger was stronger than his fear. Hesitation gone, he darted forward. Up he jumped, onto a stone that held up part of the grill. Heat struck through the pads of his paws, but he seized a corner of the steak. A blob of hot fat landed on his nose. He wanted to yelp, but he held the yelp in.

The hot meat seared his mouth. He let go of it, gulped a mouthful of air, then his jaws closed on it again. He jerked it off the grill and jumped down onto the ground. His whole body was quivering.

The meat slapped against his shoulder; hot grease burned him. Again he dropped the steak, then picked it up and began to run. It kept smacking against his legs, almost tripping him.

It was cooling off now. He dragged it deep into the bushes, but it caught on briars. He tugged and tugged, trying to pull it free.

The boy with the pail—now it was full of water— came back to the tent. "Hey," he said to his tentmate, "better put the steak on right now—it's so thick, it'll take a while to cook."

"I did put it on," said the other boy, coming out of the tent. He was carrying a skillet with a pat of butter in it—making ready to melt the butter, then fry potatoes and onions.

"Where *is* the steak?" asked the boy with the bucket.

"It's gone!" said the other. They began to look all around the fireplace.

"Hey!" one of the boys called out to the other campers. "Our steak's gone! Did anybody see our steak?"

Men, women and children came hurrying to help the boys look for it.

"Bears!" cried a frightened woman. "It must have been a bear took it."

"There's a bear around!" screamed another woman.

She made her husband run off to get a Park ranger.

Some of the campers began to look for sticks and stones. "Bears are afraid of loud noises," said one of the men. "Let's scare 'em off. I'm going to get me a couple of saucepans and bang 'em together, see?" He hurried away importantly.

The others, too, brought pans or pots. Then they all ran around the edge of the camp grounds, yelling and beating their hardware together.

Not far away, in the bushes, Tough Enough had put up his startled ears. In all his life he had never heard such a hullabaloo. It scared him, but he kept tugging at the meat in his long effort to pull it free of the briars.

The campers didn't come near him. They were afraid to venture into the brush, for fear of lurking bears.

At last the dog put all his weight and strength into a sudden pull, a desperate jerk that tore the steak loose. The campers were making so much noise, they didn't hear him dragging it over dry leaves and snapping twigs. His lower jaw dripping saliva, he carried it to the place where Sassy was waiting. With a firm paw planted on it he bolted down as much as his yearning stomach could hold.

Then he and the pony moved off into the night, away from the camp and the campers. Tough Enough carried the rest of the steak in his mouth.

7

IT was hard for Sassy to find grass, here in the forests of the Great Smoky Mountains. Tall dense trees cut off most of the light that grass needed, to grow. The pony missed the lush meadows on the Tatum farm, the oats that had helped to give him strength. He foraged mainly on leaves of young saplings and on the slender twigs of bushes.

Both animals were lean. Their ribs showed plainly, and Sassy's hipbones stuck out. Their coats had lost all luster and had a ragged look. Tough Enough no longer moved lightly, for the pads of his paws were sore. Little burrs and thorns sometimes stuck between his toes; he would stop and gnaw at them. Hunger was gradually cutting down his strength. But through the dragging minutes he and the pony kept plodding on, and the minutes turned into hours and the hours into days.

They had climbed to lofty ground close to the Park's southeast boundary when they heard distant hounds

giving tongue, from far below. The hounds were in full cry, as if they had struck a fresh trail and had started to follow it. Sassy and Tough Enough had often heard just such distant sounds in the mountains back of the Tatum farm. They did not stop their onward push.

Little by little the deep singing changed. It was splitting up—coming in sharp, short, eager bursts. Plainly the trail was growing hot, the pack was nearing its quarry.

As that grim chorus came ever louder and fiercer, the dog and the pony grew apprehensive. Tough Enough gave an asking growl.

Sassy halted. He looked down at the dog, his eyes large with alarm, then he swung his head high, nostrils flaring, ears thrust forward. He lifted a foot and stamped it down. A harsh sound, shrill with warning, forced itself out of his throat.

All of a sudden, five half-starved hounds came crackling out of dry brush. They were panting, their sides heaving, for they had been racing uphill. Ugly-looking mongrels—the biggest a Plott hound—they seemed little else but skin and bones and sinews. They bared savage teeth. They fixed their eyes—staring, red-rimmed—on Tough Enough and Sassy.

Their owners, poor mountain farmers, had not given them enough to eat. So the gaunt creatures had banded together. They were experienced marauders: killers of chickens, calves, sheep and other dogs.

The shock of danger poured new strength into Tough Enough. His dragging weakness ended on a surge of excited blood. Forgotten was the pain of sore paws. His ears went back, the skin above his spine tingled, every hair erect. He snarled fiercely.

The pony was showing his teeth and the gleaming whites of his eyes. He knew he must fight for his life and for Tough Enough. His dull fatigue was gone; his old energy and speed came back. He did not wait to be attacked. With a shrill trumpeting he charged. In mid course he swerved sharply and lashed out with his hoofs. One of the hounds, struck squarely in the ribs, went flying as if hit by a mighty hammer.

Swinging part way around, the pony reared, forefeet poised, then brought his hoofs down on a mongrel who had turned tail, surprised by the onslaught. The blow sent him sprawling. He struggled to his feet and dragged himself away.

For a moment, the three hounds who were left were full of startled confusion. They had never before picked a victim of this sort, a pony with the blood of wild horses in his veins.

Recovering their courage, they began to circle Sassy, keeping at a cautious distance, but now and then making short, threatening rushes. Again and again he charged them, but they were as cunning as wolves, skilled at swerving and dodging and leaping out of reach.

The pony's coat was dark with sweat, whitely flecked with lather. Fatigue had begun to drag at him again, but he was fighting it.

The big Plott hound—he seemed to be the leader—was the slyest and most persistently aggressive. After each retreat he had darted forward so smoothly that his body seemed to flow. Now he was ready, watching, waiting.

He saw his chance. He sprang at one of Sassy's legs, to slash the large tendon there.

The hounds had paid little heed to Tough Enough; Sassy had been the menace. But Tough Enough had not stood still. He was much quicker and nimbler than any of the hounds many times his size. A bundle of taut nerves and wiry muscles, he had been here, there and everywhere, dodging Sassy's hoofs, snarling at Sassy's attackers, now and then getting in a nip and darting away.

Now, as the Plott hound leaped at Sassy, Tough Enough jumped, too, at twice the speed. Before the hound's teeth could close on the pony's leg, Tough Enough seized one of his long, limp ears. His jaws closed and gripped and held.

The hound's head swiveled convulsively. He missed his aim. Yelping, he whirled round and round, trying to shake the dog off. Tough Enough, sailing in circles, hung on.

Sassy turned to look. Instantly the other two hounds rushed at him. He swung around to defend himself. He drove them many yards away, but not before one of them had made a long gash in his left shoulder.

The Plott hound, still trying to rid himself of Tough Enough, went wheeling close to a tree. The little dog felt a stunning blow, a flash of intense pain as he was slammed against the trunk. His grip loosened. He dropped to the ground.

The big hound stood for an uncertain moment, panting and dizzy. Then his jaws, eager to seize and crush, groped downward. They opened, reaching for Tough Enough's backbone.

Before they could close, Sassy's hoofs flashed into action. They shot out. They caught the Plott hound in the flank and sent him, howling, off into the bushes.

With their leader out of the fight, the two remaining mongrels had had enough. They went slinking off. Silently, with heads and tails low, they padded away into green dimness.

Even after they had disappeared, the dog and the pony stayed alert, suspicious. Both were trembling. Would the hounds come back, perhaps from a different direction?

Minutes passed, long and watchful and waiting. Now and then, Tough Enough would lick at a sluggish trickle of blood meandering down Sassy's left foreleg. Little by little the flow lessened. Finally it stopped.

Summer scents and sounds had been coming out of

the woods: the aromatic smell of sun-warmed resin oozing from pines; the honey fragrance of sourwood blossoms; the call of a flicker, a single note repeated very fast: *wet-wet-wet-wet-wet-wet-wet* — but no scents or noises that might mean new danger.

Tough Enough relaxed. His legs let his body down until he was lying on the trampled ground in a weary half-daze. The pony's muzzle dipped lower and lower.

After a rest, Sassy lifted his head. He shook himself. As if that were a signal, Tough Enough stood up slowly. The fight had left him stiff and aching. A faint protest, part growl and part whine, came squeezing out of his throat. Gently he and Sassy touched noses. Once more they began to push themselves along.

As they plodded onward at a slackening pace, their stiffness eased a little; but their weariness increased. Tough Enough's tail was drooping. Loss of blood had weakened Sassy still more. His feet dragged and, twice, he stumbled. Both animals had to take frequent rests.

When the round blaze of the morning sun was burning well up in the sky, they reached a hot dusty lane. They followed it to a wider dirt road, slowly moving down into a valley. Some deep awareness told them it was taking them toward home. But their strength was almost gone.

Suddenly Tough Enough whimpered; his nose had picked up an absorbing scent. It seemed familiar . . . could it be . . . ? A tingle of excitement raced along his spine. That scent—it was growing stronger—yes, that scent was Beanie's!

A warm feeling flowed all through him; he began to give eager cries. Hope brought him new strength. It went down into his legs; they sent him forward briskly; it spread all along his tail and made it whip back and forth.

Following Beanie's trail he picked up other nearby scents: Ma Tatum's, then Pa's—and next, mixed together and crisscrossing, Buck's trail and Irby's and Serena's and Annie Mae's. And all the while his excitement was yipping out of his throat.

The pony gave a questioning whinny. He was forcing himself to follow the dog, but lagging heavily behind; often Tough Enough had to stop and wait, yapping at Sassy to urge him on.

At last they drew near a little white church. Tough Enough led Sassy to the door. His new-found energy was leaving him. He crawled up three steps, each an aching effort. The pony was close behind him, unsteady at the knees.

They went through the door, open to let in fresh air, and began to walk uncertainly along the middle aisle. Church members were standing up, loudly singing a hymn. In front, the minister, erect and facing them, was joining in.

He was the first to see the dog and the pony. He stopped singing abruptly. Other people, too, caught sight of the animals. A startled man in a back pew, then another and still another, moved out into the aisle to catch them. But before the men could stop them, Tough Enough had found the Tatums. He uttered a high, hoarse, squeezed-out bark, almost like a scream. He did his best to jump up on Beanie, but his legs gave way beneath him. He dropped down at Beanie's feet and lay there with his nose touching one of Beanie's shoes.

The pony went dragging close to Beanie. He was almost too weak to stand, but he pushed his soft muzzle against the boy's neck. He nickered gently. Beanie hugged him. Then he picked Tough Enough up in his arms and pressed his cheek against the little dog's head. Mixed feelings were swirling in him. He was almost bursting with joy—but full of sorrow, too, to see how thin and weak both animals were.

Pa Tatum led Sassy out of the church, and to the old truck. Beanie and the other Tatums followed.

Men helped Pa lift the pony up into the truck; he didn't weigh much now. They laid him on the floor. Beanie and the other young Tatums climbed up into the back. Serena sat down close to Sassy. She lifted his head into her lap and cradled it there and stroked it.

"We'll be leavin' directly," Pa told the men who had helped. "We'll take these poor critters home and nurse 'em and feed 'cm till they feel frisky again, full o' git up and git."

Safe in Beanie's arms, Tough Enough closed his eyes. Slowly he opened one of them. It was a happy eye. Now, at last, he and the pony were back with the people they loved. They were going home.